N

COVERED BRIDGES
OF CENTRAL AND EASTERN CANADA

Lower Forty-five. Ruisseau Forty-five Brook, Fundy National Park, Albert County, New Brunswick. Viewed from below. This is one of New Brunswick's prettiest bridges.

COVERED BRIDGES
OF CENTRAL AND EASTERN CANADA

Lyn and Richard Harrington

McGraw-Hill Ryerson Limited

Toronto   Montreal   New York   London   Sydney

Johannesburg   Mexico   Panama   Düsseldorf

São Paulo   Kuala Lumpur   New Delhi   Auckland

Covered Bridges of Central and Eastern Canada

1 2 3 4 5 6 7 8 9 0   BP   5 4 3 2 1 9 8 7 6

Printed and bound in Canada

Canadian Cataloguing in Publication Data

Harrington, Lyn, 1911-
    Covered bridges of central and eastern Canada

ISBN 0-07-082406-1

1. Covered bridges — Canada. 2. Covered bridges —New Brunswick.
3. Covered bridges — Quebec (Province). I. Harrington, Richard, 1911-
II. Title.

TG26.H37   917.1′04′644   C76-017123-8

Contents

Foreword

IN THIS present day, apart from our longest covered bridge, which spans the mighty St. John River, most of the covered bridges may be found in villages, rural communities and in secluded wooded valleys, where streams run fresh and clear.

Here, in early spring when the alder-bud bursts to the size of a squirrel's ear, it is good to stand fishing in tune with the current, casting out and reeling in. Or, in midsummer to picnic and rest on a green slope in the shade of the bridge.

Aesthetically, as well as historically, it is urgent that we guard and preserve our remaining covered bridges — set up by co-operative "frolics" through the skilled hand labour of our grandfathers. Having thought a great deal about how these unique structures might continue to serve traffic, while remaining an ornament in the landscape, I have come to the realization that, in order to survive, our covered bridges must be valued, to ensure that they will be kept in constant repair.

How especially pleased I was, therefore, to learn that Lyn and Richard Harrington were planning a book of descriptions and photographs of the covered bridges of eastern Canada.

Their research and enthusiasm will give added impetus to the growing desire of private citizens, voluntary agencies and government officials, to care for these still useful weathered links with our past.

I feel sure that their book will be widely appreciated and treasured not only in Canada and the United States, but in many other places where people are aware of their traditions and heritage.

Thorn Cottage,   MILTON GREGG
Fredericton, New Brunswick,
Canada

Preface

WE DROVE through our first covered bridge in 1948 at Hartland, New Brunswick, the longest covered bridge in the world. Like many Canadians, we had assumed that covered wooden bridges were uniquely Yankee, part of the picturesque lore of the New England States. We learned that there were several hundred such bridges in the province and as many more in the adjoining province of Quebec, that they were not just museum pieces but living history, in constant daily use.

But we looked in vain for a book of information about these links with our past. Some ten years later, the New Brunswick Tourist Development Branch issued a helpful brochure, and in 1969 Quebec's Direction générale du tourisme followed suit.

Both of these pamphlets are updated from time to time, but with each edition the list of bridges has shortened. There was no time to lose if we wished to record them before they vanished completely.

Thus in May of 1974 and again in '75, with the aid of a modest travel grant from the Canada Council, we tracked down as many as possible. In New Brunswick we visited all 113 covered bridges then standing. A number of them spanned tidal waters. Some were interspersed with a span of open steel bridging. Though most consisted of a single span, some had five or more spans.

Also in 1975, we revisited covered bridges in Quebec and looked up others. Although 130 bridges are listed in *Ponts couverts au Québec*, the list is out of date for our tally is nearer to 80.

We studied the covered bridges in springtime, because then you can see the structure clearly. Once the trees and bushes leaf out, the form is often obscured. It would be fascinating to see them at other times — in snow, in flood-times, in autumn colouring, or to catch a Mennonite horse and buggy crossing Ontario's single covered bridge.

Newfoundland and Western Canada never boasted any covered wooden bridges, while three survived in Nova Scotia until a decade ago.

The provinces of New Brunswick and Quebec have the greatest concentrations in the world.

Covered bridge-hunting is a hobby with surprises. You never know quite where the bridge is. They are usually located on sideroads off sideroads, and some are closed to traffic.

Tracking down the bridges is often frustrating and time-consuming. We had to ask for detailed directions time and again, sometimes despairing of meeting anyone to query on the little-travelled dirt roads. In Quebec, we had only the government brochure for guidance; in New Brunswick, a special detailed set of maps, and still we had to backtrack at times.

Without exception people were friendly, but sometimes an old lady rocking on her verandah wouldn't remember the covered bridge a mile down the road. A garage man insisted there was no covered bridge on the road ahead. *"N'a plus,"* he said. But there it still sat. He was too used to seeing it.

But we also had a provincial policeman in Quebec stop beside the road and use his car radio to find out about existing bridges for us. In New Brunswick's military training area, Base Gagetown, we had a military escort to drive us by map and compass through the out-of-bounds bombing range.

Although this book is not definitive, we hope that it will spur interest in a diminishing heritage, and that others will find pleasure in learning about these historic structures and adding details to the record.

LYN AND RICHARD HARRINGTON

I

The Romance
of Covered Bridges

"THERE's another kissing bridge!" exclaims the delighted tourist
motoring on back roads of the provinces of New Brunswick and Quebec.
Tourists label any covered bridge with the nickname which purists
insist belongs only to one — a long-gone covered bridge that spanned
a millstream at 51st Street in New York City.

Every young man in the horse-and-buggy days felt it his right to give
Dobbin a breather in a covered bridge while he snatched a kiss from
the girl beside him. On a hot summer day, who could blame them for
dallying in the cool gloom? Or in the quiet evening, with the last
swallows twittering sleepily from their mud nests in the rafters overhead,
what more natural than to take advantage of the privacy offered?

And even today, when the car has replaced Dobbin, you find paired
initials and hearts entwined carved on the old timbers.

1

You may find the hippie creed, "Love is Beautiful" in highway paint, or a scrawl in crayon, "Helen is bootful."

"Sparkin' " bridges may promote romances, but wooden bridges were not covered for privacy. Nor were they enclosed for the benefit of school children waiting for the school bus, and exercising their pencils on the interior walls of the bridge. Interestingly enough, though all of the covered bridges bore names and initials, only four in New Brunswick carried obscene graffiti, and none did in Quebec.

Then why were they covered, if not to shelter people? "It's like when ladies wore lots of petticoats" goes the hoary joke, "It was to protect their underpinnings."

Wooden bridges were enclosed to protect the large timbers, the side trusses, the bracing and the supporting chords.

"Uncovered, she'll last ten–fifteen years," builders of old declared. "Put on a roof and she'll do for seventy–eighty years." And they were right. The bridge at Powerscourt, over the Chateauguay River, Huntingdon County, Quebec, has stood staunchly since 1881 requiring little repair. The only surviving covered bridge in Ontario was built that same year. The earliest known date of any New Brunswick bridge is 1895, Silver Hill bridge over the Hammond River, Kings County, replaced in 1975.

But local lore considers the one at Nelson Hollow, Northumberland County, still more venerable. The earliest date on a Quebec covered bridge is 1835, near Cookshire, over the Eaton River, Brome County. Though now by-passed, it is clearly a replacement for an older structure.

At first only the trusses (the sides) were boxed in. But such covering didn't protect the deck (carriageway) which bore the traffic, and received the most wear and tear.

Around the cracker barrel at the general store men brought out sundry good reasons for building the barnlike enclosure over a wooden bridge.

The covering protects the wood from the weather. Moisture seeps in to rot the uncovered joints in summer, or to freeze and expand them in winter. The sun beating down dries out planks, causing them to shrink and curl. If you soaked the planks in oil or tar for preservation

Smithtown. Hammond River, Kings County, New Brunswick.

they become slippery in a rain. All of these problems could be mitigated by putting on a roof and nailing on some siding.

"Roofing and siding are cheap and easy compared with building a new bridge or replacing the big beams," some opined.

Heavy snowfalls had to be plowed off open bridges as off roads, leaving a bank of snow on either side. " 'Course snow has to be shovelled *onto* the deck of a covered bridge!"

3

Nelson Hollow. Mill Brook ¼ mile above its junction with the Miramichi River near Doaktown, Northumberland County, New Brunswick. Out of service for years, this oldest (undated) of New Brunswick's covered bridges forms the focus of a wayside picnic park. Note: cottage roof, crosswise planking, Town truss. The exact date of this picturesque old bridge is not known, but old-timers remember it from the time they were children and put the date as the 1880s or early '90s. The road through the hollow is now used by only one family, the Lyons, and occasional picnickers and snowmobilers. The Lyons' home was originally "a place of entertainment," a stagecoach inn where the horses were changed. The best view of the pretty setting is from the immense trestle over the hollow, on Route 8. It is planned that the area around the bridge will become a park with the aid of the local historical society.

"People used to come down in buggies and sit there courting," Mrs. May Lyons remembered. "The hill is terrible for icing in fall and winter. Many's the time Mr. Lyons had to get up out of bed, hitch up the horses, to get some car up the hill. Often cars spin right around on the hill in winter."

Snowmobilers using the bridge "snow-pave" it before attempting to cross. In spring, the slopes of the hill are thick with purple violets and wild strawberries, and the brooksides lavish with fiddlehead ferns. The trout fishing in the brisk little river is said to be excellent.

And there was always someone to see it from the horse's point of view. Horses generally fear rushing water, and no less when they had to look down and see it below their hoofs through shrunken planks. (Try looking down when you run across an old bridge sometime, and you'll share the horse's alarm.)

Sometimes a skittish trotter stubbornly refused to cross an open wooden bridge, the reverberation of its hoofs were so unnerving. Some reared in fright and even bolted.

Yet these same creatures would trot docilely up to the entrance of a covered bridge. It was reassuringly similar to that of a stable entrance. The drumming of their hoofs and the rumble of the carriage wheels were alarming, but there were comforting walls on either side, and daylight at the end of the wooden tunnel.

The covered bridge did provide brief protection from the elements for man and beast. It was a fine place to rest the horses before tackling the hill at the other end — for many covered bridges are set on a slope, with a right-angled turn at each end.

It was a good place to take shelter with a load of hay, waiting for a break in the clouds. A blizzard's blast was temporarily thwarted in the lee of the wooden walls — providing it wasn't blowing a headwind. For the covered bridge acts like a breezeway or chimney. "Pulls the draft," they used to say. Road crews of today declare they prefer to work in the open rather than inside a covered bridge. "Coldest place this side o' Hell!"

The covered bridge was and still is, a good place for school children to foregather on their way to and from school. Some meet the school bus there, as their parents used to meet the school van. The van was a twenty-foot box, set on wheels in summer, and transferred to runners in winter.

Small boys still force a gap in the siding of the covered bridge, and play "follow the leader", leaping from the bridge into the water below, holding their noses. They still swing from a rope attached to a lower chord or stringer and drop into a pool shaded by the bridge. Fishermen, too, love the shady pool under the bridge, where trout and salmon rest in the cool water.

Bamford–Colpitts. Coverdale River, Albert County, New Brunswick. Covered bridges were good places to advertise.

In times past, the covered bridges were notable places to advertise patent medicines, a coming circus or an election. An oculist whose practice was, hopefully, better than his spelling, advertised in the Bamford–Colpitts bridge over Coverdale River, Albert County, N.B. "Eye glasses corectly fitted." Evangelical zeal made sure that sinners were warned of their ways. Even the darkness wasn't concealing when you knew a text boldy proclaimed "THOU GOD SEEST ME." The walls of the covered bridges still carry signs, but they, too, have changed in tone.

Nowadays, only the government is allowed to post notices on government structures. Hence most messages are from the provincial departments of Agriculture or Fisheries, warning farmers not to wash chemicals out of their sprayers in fresh running water. The chemicals poison the fish which are a major sport attraction in New Brunswick and Quebec.

Circus posters of early days are replaced by messages from the government. These two on the boards protecting the important end timbers are warnings from the Dept. of Agriculture and the Dept. of Fisheries. Note: inward slope of the portal also to protect the end timbers from weather.

Painted signs demanding that you "WALK YOUR HORSES OR PAY TWO DOLLARS FINE" have gone from the portals of the covered bridges. Occasionally the raised letters remain, painted over but still legible. One such is the Hartley Steeves Bridge in Albert County, N.B. The Lockhart Mill bridge, over the Shikatehawk River, in Carleton County, N.B., still bears the old sign repainted by an artistic historian a few years before her death. She had fiercely defended the bridge when it was in danger of replacement.

Another elderly lady admitted, "We girls didn't mind much about speed limit, when we had to drive home at night. We just slapped the reins to make the horses go faster to get out of a covered bridge. We were always scared to drive through them at night. They were so dark. Very few of them were lighted at night."

The covered bridges were also labelled "Wishing bridges".

Legend says that if you make a wish while passing through a covered bridge, holding your breath and with your eyes closed until the driver sounds the horn as you exit, your wish will come true. But not if the driver makes a wish too!

Tales of ghosts and murders in the covered bridges are rare and are not, as a rule, trotted out for the stranger. Who could blame anyone walking through a dark creaking covered bridge on a windy night for imagining the presence of spirits? There is a persistent tale that a man drowned when the Upper Dorchester bridge over the Memramcook River, Westmorland County, N.B., was swept away in the flood of 1917. His body was never recovered, but no one has seen his ghost.

Dr. Helen Creighton of Halifax, Nova Scotia, gathering material for her book, *Bluenose Ghosts*, learned that "bridges are favourite haunts for spirits, largely because they have so often been the scene of tragedies". Boys frolicking, planks breaking, floods, carriages missing the turn and driving off the bridge, drunks missing the portal. . . . Until recently there was a covered bridge at Avonsport, the last surviving such in Nova Scotia. Here, according to report, a woman in white used to appear, not only at night but also in the daytime. Scarier still, Dr. Creighton was told of the ghost of a headless man, who used to come out at the Lake Bennett covered bridge near Elgin, Albert County, N.B.

Both of these bridges are now gone, and Dr. Creighton "often wonders what happens to ghosts when the places they frequent are taken away or changed completely".

Most of our informants knew nothing of robberies or hold-ups in covered bridges, but the notion did persist.

A retired bridge engineer recalled an anecdote from his youth.

"My uncle was a doctor in Boiestown, Northumberland County, [N.B.,] and he was held up in the covered bridge that used to be there. He was coming home late from a professional call, and was just nicely within the bridge when two men dropped on him from the arches. They had climbed into the rafters, ready to fall on the doctor as he trudged beneath. The victim went limp — no point in provoking his assailants to more violence than they had perhaps intended — until they went for his wallet! That galvanized the doctor, who struck out with might and main.

"Bodies went flying, let me tell you," chuckled the engineer. "My uncle knocked them right and left, and would have chucked them into the Miramichi, except they shouted. It turned out to be a couple of his

Hoyt Station. Back Creek, Sunbury County, New Brunswick. Note: square portals.

friends, playing a practical joke that backfired. Country fellows used to play lots of practical jokes in those days."

Mr. & Mrs. Russell Knorr of Oromocto, N.B. have fond memories of the Smye Bridge near their home. The bridge was built in 1915, one of many built by A. E. Smye, and Mrs. Knorr's brother was one of the carpenters. Locally, it's still called the Smye Bridge, though the N.B. Department of Highways prefers to label it "No. 599, South Oromocto River #2." That means it is the second bridge over the South Branch of the Oromocto River and its individual departmental number is 599. Since every bridge maintained by the Department carries its own individual number, for ready identification, the covered bridges

9

Hartland. Saint John River at Hartland, Carleton County, New Brunswick. At 1282 feet, it is the longest covered bridge in the world comprising eight spans.

The first bridge across the river at this point was built in 1898–99 by the Hartland Bridge Company who opened it as a toll bridge. A sign read, "5¢ per person. 10¢ per team." The structure was taken over by the New Brunswick Provincial Government in 1904 and made free of tolls.

The original bridge consisted of seven Howe truss spans on cedar cribwork abutments and stone-filled piers. These were replaced in 1920 with concrete piers and abutments. Some people in Hartland still remember the construction of the 1920 bridge for they helped to build it. Others remember its 1898 forerunner. Until recently, the newer bridge bore the sign, "20 Dollars Fine for Driving Faster than a Walk over this Bridge."

Automobile drivers were apt to speed up for the steep hill at the western end. When cars became wider, only one at a time could use the bridge, and congestion became a problem. Recently a new high concrete bridge was opened across the St. John, within sight of its forerunner downstream, a couple miles above Hartland, on the Trans-Canada Highway.

Another unusual feature of the Hartland bridge is that it is electrically lighted, and there is a boxed-in sidewalk along the south side, added in 1943, lighted by permanent louvres and electricity. Hartland bridge is famous too for the salmon pool below. You can hang out the windows and watch the salmon anglers wade out into the swirling waters. Famous raconteur Will Bird of Halifax, spins a yarn that fishermen farther downstream were feeding the migrating salmon. The fish were so hyped-up that when they reached the covered bridge, they simply leaped over it. Fishermen had to arrange for sky-hooks to catch 'em.

were no exception. They were also identified as to their location on the river, No. 1 being nearest the mouth. Kennebacasis River, No. 23 was thus the 23rd covered bridge from the mouth of this long winding stream.

Previous to the building of the Smye Bridge, Russ Knorr used to haul pulp and cordwood out of the bush where he had hand-cut it with a bucksaw. It took a whole day to haul one load to the Hoyt railway station, woodsmen having to cross the Oromocto River on the ice at the ford and to find the easiest way up the hill.

Mrs. Knorr remembers corn boils on the flats which now have been turned into a picnic park. "We had a barrel of fun," she chuckles. "We'd have square dancing on the floor of the Smye Bridge, not to a fiddle but to an accordion. The men brought kerosene lanterns and hung them on the bridge and on the trees."

Even today only a few covered bridges boast illumination, and that by electricity — for example, the remarkable Hartland Bridge, Carleton County, N.B., the longest covered bridge in the world.

A few Indian names were used for the covered bridges in memory of the Micmacs and Maliseets, who, before the white man moved in, roamed the waterways and made the portage trails that grew into by-roads and into today's highways. Milkish, in Kings County, N.B., means "the place where food is dried". Plumweseep, and Kouchibouguac were others.

Legend grew up around several of these covered bridges. The Harry Jonah Bridge, a picturesque old-timer built in 1912 near Elgin, Albert County, was named for H. R. Jonah, a farmer who happened to be driving a herd of cattle across the former bridge when it collapsed, leaving poor Harry the butt of rustic jokes, such as "Too much bull on that bridge".

The Harris Steeves Bridge at Salem, Albert County, won the soubriquet "Dan Cupid's Bridge", when in 1923 the construction engineer, John Forbes met and married a local girl. The Hartley Steeves Bridge is half a mile down the road, named, presumably for a brother, and they are often called twin bridges, though the Harris is 7 feet longer. No two covered bridges can be identical.

Hartley Steeves. Bull Creek in Salem, Albert County, New Brunswick. Its "twin", the Harris Steeves Bridge, ½ mile away spans Weldon Creek.

The Ryan Bridge, Nashwaak No. 9, York County, N.B., was labelled "the bridge to Nowhere". Built in 1908 to sweeten an influential politician, who was dreaming of a larger bailiwick, it stood unused until dismantled in 1971. For the planned settlement never materialized, and the road on both sides went back to bush.

Some now-vanished bridges of New Brunswick acquired the distinction of a legend or at least a nickname. For instance, the bridge

Sign over Hartley Steeves Bridge, which was nicknamed "Dan Cupid Bridge".
Note: reversal of the name and the omission of the comma.

over Eliot Brook was moved there from the Shikatehawk River, Carleton
County, in 1930, and consequently tagged "the travelling bridge", like
many another such. It was more economical to move a bridge no longer
needed in its original position than to build a new one from scratch.

Bridges were generally named for their location, such as Hardscrabble
Hill Bridge, Big Marsh, Burnt Church River No. 1 Mouth, Johnson
Schoolhouse Bridge. Others were named for the nearest landowner,
"who in return for this distinction, was expected to look after the
bridge's welfare, report defects to the road builders, and speed-demons
to the authorities". At one time the task of "snow-paving the bridge" fell
to this person. This consisted of spreading snow over the floor of the
bridge to insure easy passage of sleighs, cutters and bobsleds. Some land-
owners' names are still in use in New Brunswick, such as the Starkey
bridge over Long's Creek, Damas Couturier in Madawaska County, and
Burpee bridge over the Gaspereau Stream in Queens County.

Some few years ago, the N.B. Department of Highways decided to
regularize the names of bridges. An over-precise clerk managed to confuse
things still more by reversing the names from, say, the Hartley Steeves
bridge to Steeves, Hartley. Stenographers, printers and signpainters
often neglected the comma. Was Bamford Colpitts bridge, Albert
County, named for Bamford or Colpitts, or was it all one name? It turned
out to be Bamford–Colpitts Bridge, named for a new settlement beyond,
a settlement that lasted only briefly.

II

The Background

MAN HAS always built his bridges from materials close at hand, whether stone, tree trunks or vines. North America, laced with creeks and rivers, called for myriad bridges; and the vast forests provided the desired hemlock, pine and spruce.

"It's the best-watered area for its size in the world," states the New Brunswicker, confidently, about his province of 28,354 square miles, and certainly it holds the greatest number of covered bridges today.

In timber countries, bridges generally were of wood as in pioneer North America, despite a climate noted for violent extremes. Builders always knew that if you protected a structure from the weather, it would last much longer. This was especially true of bridges which lay open to rain and snow, vulnerable to decay.

It is said that some roofed bridges have existed in China for two thousand years, frequently repaired, of course. But the first recorded covered bridge is said to have spanned the Euphrates River back in 783 B.C. London Bridge in Elizabethan days had a narrow covered walkway for pedestrians threading their way between crowded shops and houses. These bridges were all built of stone.

The covering of *wooden* bridges was a novel idea, one that reached its greatest development in North America. Lucerne, Switzerland boasts two covered wooden bridges. Chapel bridge, built in 1333, bears remarkable paintings of local history on its ceiling. The smaller Spreuer Bridge built in 1407 is decorated with a grim Dance of Death. A very long covered bridge of 1082 feet was built in Norway. But the longest covered bridge in the world is the 1282-foot bridge at Hartland, N.B. spanning the Saint John River.

Before and after white settlers came to New Brunswick, the paddles and canoes of Maliseet and Micmac Indians furrowed the great rivers of New Brunswick and those of other Indian tribes left their wake in the great rivers of Quebec. The sea was the main highway for the Atlantic provinces, as the St. Lawrence River was for Quebec, and the Great Lakes for Ontario. The pioneers travelled by boat as much as possible to avoid the horribly rough corduroy roads, made of logs laid side by side over which horses slipped and heaved, and wagons lurched.

In 1763 came the end of the Seven Years' War in Europe, when Acadia and New France became part of British North America, and of present-day Canada.

Settlers came from New England and from the British Isles. They paid five pounds for 100 acres of uncleared land, and higher prices for farms vacated by the Acadian French.

After the American Revolution (1775–83), colonists loyal to England were exiled from the young United States of America. These United Empire Loyalists, and others attracted by low-priced land pushed north into the eastern part of British North America, which in 1867 became the provinces of Nova Scotia, New Brunswick, Quebec and Ontario. The Loyalists were given land grants to compensate them for their losses in England's former colonies. They still looked south

15

for expertise.

The first patent for a covered wooden bridge was taken out by a private company in 1797, for a bridge over the Schuylkill River in Philadelphia. A span of 1300 feet was planned and built as an open bridge. Engineer Timothy Palmer could well be proud of his workmanship when the Market Street bridge was formally opened in 1804. A prudent member of the bridge company, looking to his investment, speculated how much longer the bridge might endure if the main timbers were sheltered from the elements.

Builder Palmer was grieved to cover his timberwork, but was consoled by the realization the covered portion of 550 feet would last longer. He was soon declaring roundly, "I am an advocate for weatherboarding and roofing, altho there are some who may say it argues much against my interests." He knew there were plenty of other rivers that need bridging.

The idea spread in all directions — from the Atlantic to California and north into Canada.

With far less money in their pockets than those who had stayed in the rebellious colonies, the United Empire Loyalists kept bridge costs

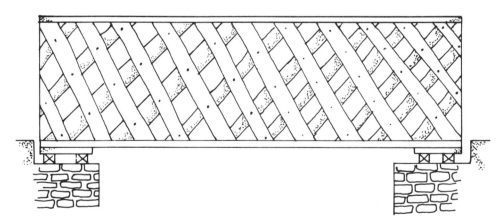

Town Lattice Truss

Coulonge. Coulonge River, Pontiac County, Quebec. Timbers in a Town truss were pegged with wooden treenails ("trunnels").

down to a minimum. There was, and is, nothing fancy about the covered bridges of New Brunswick. They look alike, varying only in detail, and very much like the weathered silvery barns in the fields beyond.

With a wealth of timber and an abundance of streams to be bridged, American architects and constructors hustled into action, and competed for contracts. Perhaps the most fervent in touting his "mode" was Ithiel Town of Connecticut, who took out a patent in 1820 for his lattice design. The heavy trusses could be built of short timbers, pinned together with wooden treenails (trunnels) and weight only tightened the framework. "You can build it to any length," Town pointed out. "Build it by the mile and sell it by the yard."

The inventor charged $1.00 a foot for the use of his "patent", or $2.00 a foot if anyone used it without first getting permission. He lived very comfortably on his royalties.

Vermont took enthusiastically to the attractive Town design, basically a continuous lattice of great strength. The lattice stiffened the truss against the wind, without presenting a solid resistance. Flood waters could pour through the bridge from one side to the other with less danger of sweeping the bridge off its pediments. Neighbouring Quebec followed Vermont's lead and built almost all its covered bridges on the Town principle. New Brunswick too, approved the Town design, until William Howe of Massachusetts improved the truss. Only one lattice bridge remains in the province, the picturesque one at Nelson Hollow, near Doaktown, Northumberland County.

The Howe truss used lighter timbers and a wider lattice. But it introduced cast-iron tension members, rods running through both upper

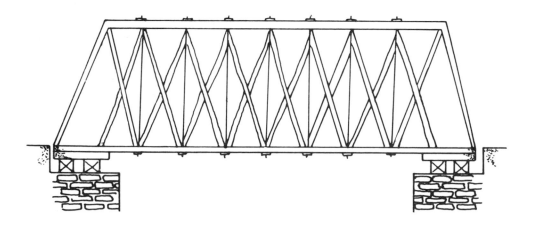

Howe Truss

Replacement. Roofing and siding removed, the Howe trusses of the former covered bridge are clearly revealed. Centre Blissville, Sunbury County, New Brunswick.

and lower chords. Howe attached nuts to the threaded ends, so that they could be tightened if the bridge showed signs of sagging. Thus the bridge could be trued with relative ease.

Bell. Trout Creek, Kings County, New Brunswick. Roof bracing and Howe truss, including iron rods at intervals.

Theodore Burr invented a laminated wooden arch to strengthen his trusses on the inside. This proved the strongest design of all, but it was difficult to repair, so its popularity was limited, though examples remain in New Brunswick. The durable bridge at Powerscourt, Que. has a curved arched roof over each of its two spans, and is believed to be the only covered bridge in the world built with the McCallum inflexible arched truss.

The earliest covered bridges in Quebec were toll bridges, built by

William Mitton. Over a tidal tributary to Turtle Creek, Albert County, New Brunswick. Has an extra wooden truss as bracing. Beyond is a railway bridge employing the Burr truss arch for extra strength.

a community or by a small private company.

Some were quite elaborate, gracious bridges painted in black and white, with facades of worked wood. Several of this sort were erected in the Eastern Townships close to the Vermont border. They had a covered walkway for pedestrians, and sometimes a centre wall between two traffic lanes. Small openings were made in the walls to let the light in and at night, a few lanterns lighted the way. Unfortunately none of these bridges have survived.

In the early decades of this century, many covered bridges were built in Quebec's out-lying counties by the provincial Department of Colonization, which then had the responsibility of opening new roads. The term "colonization bridges" is used for many in the vast Abitibi county.

Powerscourt. Chateauguay River near Elgin, Huntingdon County, Quebec. Built in 1881, this is the oldest covered bridge in the province, with two McCallum fixed arches over two spans.

In New Brunswick, too, some bridges were built by men who had no engineering training but who had subsidics from the government, which was eager to promote roads and bridges. For instance, the Journal of the House of Assembly of New Brunswick recorded, "Passed 1st March, 1824 to Samuel Freeze, the sum of 100 pounds, to assist him in rebuilding the bridge over the Kennebecassis [sic] on the great road of communication, which bridge was built by him in the year 1817, and was to be maintained till 1827 — the same having been lately carried away by an unusual rise of water."

And again, "Thursday, 17th March 1831 the sum of 50 pounds to Dominicus Miliken to remunerate him in part for building a bridge over the Maggaguadavic [sic] River."

In the records the word "covered" is not always applied specifically to the bridges. It was evidently taken for granted and the clue comes

Stillwater. Digdeguash River, Charlotte County, New Brunswick.

only in the list of building materials.

Sometimes the construction of a bridge aroused heated arguments as to which parish or county would benefit most from its building. A jury might well be called in to decide what each should contribute, but this was not always necessary. Mr. E. Botsford, Commissioner of Roads for the province of New Brunswick, reported in 1840 that he had "contracted for the building of a bridge to be constructed upon Piles over the Missiguash River, for the sum of 270 pounds, one half of this Contract is to be borne by the Province of Nova Scotia."

Commissioner Botsford was evidently a careful man, not least with the public funds. He ended his 1840 report, "We humbly trust that the amount we have recommended to be granted toward the completion of this Road will not be considered extravagant . . . . a sum of 160 pounds remains in the Treasury. This amount has been reserved for

Benton. Eel River, York County, New Brunswick.

putting a new Covering on the Nackawickack [*sic*] Bridge, which is very much required; the materials are on the ground . . . but I would remark that the sum reserved will hardly be sufficient to complete the work....." Succeeding Road Commissioners were equally conscientious.

Road commissioners had examined the Oromocto River from its mouth, looking for "the most eligible place to erect a bridge". They found an excellent site, owned by a George Morrow, who refused to give up his property. He wanted to build his home on the grounds. If the commissioners insisted on expropriating his land, he would set the value at a startling 200 pounds. He even offered 25 pounds towards

Flume Ridge. Magaguadavic River, Charlotte County, New Brunswick.

West Montrose. Waterloo County, Ontario. North portal and east side.

Irish River. Vaughan Creek, Saint John County, New Brunswick.

the bridge construction if only they would build it somewhere else.
This was a generous offer, or bribe.

A couple of local business men were more amenable. "We'll give
you the right of way free," they offered, "if you'll carry the road past
our door."

The Commissioners sadly shook their heads. This route wasn't
nearly so suitable, and it would cost more than 200 pounds to shore
up the broken uneven banks of the river at this point.

The Commissioners called together a jury, and they and Morrow
put their cases to the panel. The jury awarded Morrow compensation
of 174 pounds. The next problem was to decide "on the best and most
secure manner of erecting said Bridge."

"After taking the best means in our power to inform ourselves, by
consulting with persons in this province, and from the United States,
who were conversant upon the subject, we were induced to believe that

Tomilson Mill. Odellach River, Victoria County, New Brunswick. Many covered bridges served pioneer mills.

one erected on Piles would be most durable and less liable to be effected [*sic*] by the ice."

John Clark, a man of practical knowledge and recommended as well qualified for the duty, inspected the site, took distances and levels, probed the river bottom, and prepared a plan with specifications as to timber and materials. This preliminary work cost 132 pounds.

At public auction, the construction was "struck off" to Jephtha S. Hubble for the sum of 994 pounds, and the guarantee that the work be completed in 13 months. Another 600 pounds had to go into building the causeway, the ramps up to bridge level.

The costs seem trifling by today's rates, but were expensive enough in those days, though labour and materials were cheap and plentiful.

The figures were set out:

Contract for the Bridge	994 pounds
Ground for the road to Morrow	174
Causeway	600
Plans, survey, etc	132
	1900 pounds

And so the first covered bridge on the Oromocto came into being. The Morrow covered bridge, possibly a replica, spanned the Oromocto in the 1950s.

By 1880, the currency had changed from pounds to dollars, and expenses had risen. "New roofing, etc. Covered Bridge" now amounted to $270.00, more than the entire cost a new bridge forty years previously. A new covering for one span at Long's Creek cost $60.00, while Kelly's Creek required a shorter span plus interior railing costing "$46.50 by days work."

Only a few of the covered bridges were ever lighted at night. In 1917, a sum was passed to light up the St. Jacques covered bridge in Madawaska County, N.B. "Lanterns and pulleys $15.60 to Eustache Francoeur — Installation of lamps $4.40; care of same to Sept. 30, 1917, $25.00 to Joseph Michaud."

The long covered Upper Dorchester bridge over the Memramcook River near Sackville, Westmorland County, was more modern. Estimates from the Eastern Electric & Development Co. Ltd. ran: Lighting bridge 5 months, Jan. 1st 1917 to June 20th, 1917 $7.50. (That autumn the bridge blew down in a gale, and there were no electricity bills for the next two years.)

Also included is the expense item "Snowing the bridge." At one time the job of snowing cost $4.00 for a winter, but had doubled to $8.00 in 1879. By 1917, it had risen substantially to $12.00 *a month*. Inflation is nothing new in highway maintenance.

Upper Dorchester. Memramcook River near Sackville, Westmorland County, New Brunswick. The river's strong current battles twice daily with the high tides of the Bay of Fundy. Note: five large log and rock piers each with prow upstream to deflect ice and debris, long windows on eastern end to give view of railway. At 848 feet this is the second longest covered bridge in Canada and probably in the world. The original bridge was blown down in a gale of 1917. One man was drowned, his body never recovered.

None of these early covered bridges remains standing. Wood wears out eventually, even when protected from the elements. But many were replaced by later versions, sometimes with the barnlike covering, sometimes by an iron bridge, and increasingly today by reinforced or pre-stressed concrete structures.

III

Building
the Covered Bridge

THE LENGTH of the covered bridge was, of course, determined by the space it had to span. Height and width were more flexible. The old rule of thumb was "It had to be high enough and wide enough to take a load of hay". It had to be strong enough to bear the weight of rollers used in road maintenance.

When there was sufficient demand for one, a bridge had to be built across a stream or an arm of the sea, over a ravine or at the narrows of a lake. After travellers had grumbled sufficiently about the delays and waste of horseflesh in having to make a round-about journey, someone took action. It might be the local or provincial government. Or it might be an enterprising merchant or miller.

The location of the bridge was hotly debated, and, as always, possible sites were studied for volume of potential traffic. The location

Aaron Clark. Canaan River, Queens County, New Brunswick.

must have reasonably good approaches, not marshy ground, for instance, nor too broken a shoreline.

A narrow place in a stream or ravine was desirable from the point of cost, as well as engineering problems. For both these reasons, bridges were set straight across rather than on a slant or curve, unless the virtue of natural rocky footings outweighed the disadvantages.

Darling's Island. Kennebecasis River, Kings County, New Brunswick. The right-angled approach is customary.

Since most pioneer roads used river valleys and often the river bank, the approach to the bridge was generally a right angle. So much the better — traffic would have to slow down to a walk, which was less destructive of the bridge.

If the bridge was financed by a private individual or company, as most were in Quebec, tolls would be charged for using the bridge. Covered bridge tolls there around 1890 ran:

Cart (two wheels) with a horse .... 5¢
Cart (with four wheels) with a horse .... 7½¢
Horse or mare .... 2½¢
Cow .... 2¢
Daily walker .... 1¢
The last tolls charged in New Brunswick were on the long span at

Hartland. Saint John River, Carleton County, New Brunswick. Hill at west portal with pretty town of Hartland at east end. Note: window openings and concrete piers pointed upstream to deflect ice and debris. Concrete piers and abutments were built in 1920, replacing the original (1897) cedar logs and rock-filled piers.

Hartland. This open bridge, nearly one quarter mile long was built by a private company. The company charged tolls of 3¢ for each person on foot and 8¢ for a single team. Traffic was not heavy enough to pay the bills, and the company was glad to sell out to the provincial government in 1904 when tolls were abolished.

Once the site was determined for a bridge, and financing settled, a builder had to be found. Government contracts had to be struck off at public auction. Private builders had more freedom of choice. The constructor hired his own crew, or he might make use of "statute labour", men wishing to work off their taxes by so many days work on the roads.

Rollingdam. Digdeguash River, Charlotte County, New Brunswick.

Abutments and piers were put in at the time of lowest water level, generally in late summer or early autumn. Where the water was shallow, usually a cofferdam of earth was sufficient to keep the site relatively dry. A clamshell-shaped scoop would be hitched to a team of plough horses and a dyke of earth piled up. If necessary, a pump could be used as well.

Most of the covered bridges consist of a single span, reaching from one abutment to the other. Quite a number, however, are of multiple spans resting on piers as well as abutments. Most of the abutments, or footings in both provinces are now of concrete.

Both piers and abutments might be of poured concrete, especially for bridges built in this century. But some were comprised of large blocks of hewn stone, as at the Peter Jonah Bridge, Albert County, N.B. Among the early settlers were many immigrants from Scotland and Ireland with stone-working experience. Or the piers could be of stout log cribs, very broad at the base, filled with rocks. A notable example

Peter Jonah. Turtle Creek, Albert County, New Brunswick. Closed-face squared log abutments and mason-cut stones in ramps.

is the long 5-span Upper Dorchester Bridge over the Memramcook River, Westmorland County, N.B. Some crib piers in Quebec had wedges pointing upstream to break up ice cakes, or to deflect floating logs away from the piers, like a pair over the Lièvre River, Labelle County, Que. These wedges are called "ice breakers" in New Brunswick.

In deep water the bridge-builders had to sink wooden cofferdams and pour concrete into forms, as at The Narrows bridge in Queens County, N.B. But the variations add interest for the covered bridge enthusiast. Builders liked experimenting.

The open-face crib is a close runner-up for abutments. This is a layer of baulks (squared logs), then a layer of flat rocks or sometimes horizontal logs chocked with shorter logs, the interstices filled with small

Capleton. Massawippi River, Compton County, Quebec. Note: unusual sheeting over Town lattice.

rocks. This is skilled work and men were proud of their handiwork. As the weight of the bridge and traffic descended on these abutments, the sandwich of logs and stones was held very firmly. Occasional closed abutments appear to be wholly of logs crosshatched, but they actually form a retaining wall for loose rocks which enhances drainage.

The ramps leading from road level to the deck of the bridge might be of any kind of stony fill, but often they, too, were evidence of the artisan's skill. Some high ramps were flanked with "riprap", large flat rocks laid in courses. An exceptionally good example is seen at the

Types of Abutments

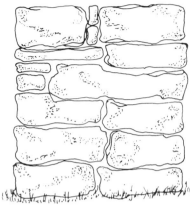

large blocks
of hand-hewn stone

log cribs

open-face cribs

Marven. Belleisle Creek, Kings County, New Brunswick. Open-face abutments of squared logs and rocks.

Dumbarton. Digdeguash River, Charlotte County, New Brunswick. Combines cut stone in one abutment with riprap in the ramp.

Narrows Bridge, over Lake Washedemoak. Some more recent ramps are buttressed by "gabions", squared nets of heavy wire filled with smaller stones.

While this work was going ahead, the construction engineer had the timbers cut to size at the nearest sawmill, and the cut boards and planks were hauled by wagon to a flat "proving" ground near the bridge site. While few settlers in the Canadian provinces were bridge-builders by profession, most had built houses and barns, and many were boat-builders.

The Narrows. Lake Washedemoak, Queens County, New Brunswick. Two covered spans separated by a steel span.

There is not a great deal of difference between building a shed over a bridge and building a barn. The construction is much the same, but the building of bridges requires more engineering skill. Some men, such as Luther Smith and A. E. Smye built many of New Brunswick's covered bridges, but most of those still standing were supervised by trained engineers, who understood the science of tension and compression, and knew how to prevent sway.

The truss timbers that form the sides of the bridge, were laid out on the proving-ground, and "framed", that is, assembled, then taken

Bell. Trout Creek, Kings County, New Brunswick. Has log and rock abutments. Ramps are composed of loose rock and gabions, wire-netted rocks.

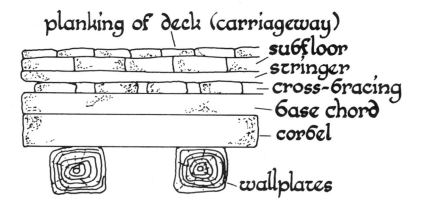

planking of deck (carriageway)
subfloor
stringer
cross-bracing
base chord
corbel
wallplates

Base of Bridge and Carriageway

Wakefield. Gatineau River, Gatineau County, Quebec.

Hartland. Saint John River, Carleton County, New Brunswick.

Keenan. Monquart River, Carleton County, New Brunswick. Underside with crossbeams and chords. The open-face abutment is a "club sandwich" of logs and rocks.

apart again before actual construction began. The heavy lower chords, the base of the bridge, went into place as soon as the piers were ready. They had a "camber" to them, a slight upward curve that would flatten with the weight of the bridge and traffic. A well-framed bridge always had some residual camber.

The heavy chords that formed the base of the bridge were slid across from the near abutment to the far abutment on the temporary bents, or the pier, with the use of ropes, men and teams. Each span, of course, was similarly based. Stout floorbeams were laid on the chords as crossbracing, and stringers laid over them lengthwise. Once the stringers were in place they were topped with a sub-floor of boards laid crosswise or diagonally, again to prevent distortion of the structure. Over this went the planking which formed the deck or carriageway.

Capleton. Massawippi River, Compton County, Quebec. Uses "tree knees" as angle bracing for the roof.

The lower chords forming the base of the bridge rested on corbels and wallplates, blocks of wood which carried the burden of the superstructure and traffic. The underside of a bridge, with its cross-beams and diagonal bracing, is fascinating to engineers.

When automotive transport became more frequent, as well as faster and heavier, builders had to make more allowance for impact and vibration, both in the trusses and in the supports.

A bridge is a complex thing of compression on some members, and tension on others. They work together to distribute the strain on the structure, especially the sudden strain of impact from a loaded truck. Trucks are banned on many of Quebec's covered bridges by the warning *"CAMION INTERDIT"* and the symbol of a truck with a slash across it, or the portal is framed with a steel arch. In some other bridges the message is even plainer. A steel barricade crosses the portal at a height just high enough to clear an automobile. Thus the bridge is reserved for light-weight traffic, which will not imperil its life. Disgruntled truckers can find an alternative crossing in some more modern bridge not too far away.

The planking was usually laid lengthwise, but it might go crosswise, or even in a herringbone design according to the preference of the builder. Many decks that are being replaced today in New Brunswick employ laminated flooring. That is, 2 × 6" boards set on edge and pressed tightly together. This makes a durable floor, which, however, has a tendency to become slippery when wet.

Nowadays the decks of covered bridges are being chip-sealed, to match the road. Hot asphalt is laid by a road-paving crew, and showered with chipped stone which the traffic works down to form a water resistant cover. The black-topping does not add to the strength of the bridge, but it saves wear on the wooden deck and avoids the slipperiness of wet planking.

Next the heavy prefabricated side trusses were slid across the new deck, and raised upright in the same way as raising the side of a barn, with teams and pulley, using a sturdy tree as a fulcrum. They were fastened in place, sometimes with treenails (trunnels), pegs of hardwood hammered into auger holes. In New Brunswick the trusses were placed piece by piece, beginning with the bottom chord, diagonals, counter braces, and finally the top chords. Especially in the larger bridges the trusses would be very heavy and unwieldy in one piece.

Next came the arched rafters, and the roof tree. Several Quebec bridges, notably the Milby and Capleton, were angle-braced with strong "tree-knees", curved roots cut to fit the arch of the roof and strengthen it. The roof could be shingled, and the "sheeting" on the sides nailed in place by ordinary carpenters, while the construction crew moved on to its next job.

On Quebec bridges the sheeting or siding is usually clapboard or tongue-and-groove nailed horizontally across the latticed sides. Invariably a gap was left up near the eaves, perhaps to prevent dry rot. Another gap about a foot wide was left at shoulder height. The gaps run the full length of the bridge to admit light and air, but they also present a less solid obstruction to wind sweeping along the river valley.

New Brunswick preferred to apply its sheeting vertically. This required a lighter strip nailed across the side trusses to which the plain

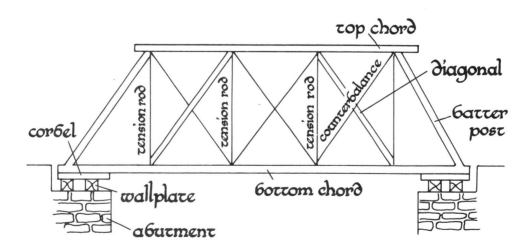

Bridge Construction

44

Point Wolfe. Point Wolfe River, Fundy National Park, Albert County, New Brunswick.

board siding could be nailed. These "purlins" made it possible to use shorter boards which were less expensive and easier to replace. However, usually, on the original bridge the vertical boards were one piece; when bridges have a row of short boards on the bottom, this is usually an indication that the bottom chords have been repaired.

Often one or more windows admit light into a covered bridge in New Brunswick. Some have hinged shutters, the reason for which is unknown today. Did New Brunswickers, like New Englanders sometimes use the covered bridge as an assembly or drill hall? Or was this thoughtless copying?

45

Often a window is cut near the end of the bridge, especially if there is the familiar right-angled turn beyond. These are relatively recent innovations, since the advent of the horseless carriage. Most bridges accommodate only a single lane of traffic, and it is helpful to be able to anticipate an oncoming car.

When the siding was new and tight, the interior of the covered bridge was as dim as a tunnel, but as the siding weathered the boards dried, the edges curled or shrunk. Shafts of sunlight form a striped pattern on the deck. Driving at a modest speed through a New Brunswick covered bridge, you find the boards no interruption to vision, for the interstices form a series of frames like a moving picture film, so that the outside scene is continuous.

The most vulnerable part of any covered bridge is the portal, and not just because of careless drivers and too-large loads. Here the sun and driving rain weather the heavy end-timbers of the side trusses and the deck. Here the wagon wheels and later pneumatic tires struck with sudden impact. To protect the important end beams the portals were usually slanted inward 12 to 18 inches. Occasionally a sort of porch extends well beyond the portal as in the West Montrose covered bridge in Ontario.

Quite the reverse occurs on several Quebec bridges, where the portals are stepped back, as at the Coulonge Bridge, Pontiac County. But each Quebec bridge has its portal lined for 5 to 8 feet with a square of clapboard or tongue-and-groove for extra protection of the end beams. In New Brunswick this additional protection is usually triangular.

Though all portals had to be able to accommodate "a load of hay", some portals are considerably higher than others, with rounded arches, where most are rectangular with bevelled corners.

Several New Brunswick bridges have an additional safeguard for the portal, a culvert dug across the road a yard or so from the lintel, as at Little Lepreau, Charlotte County. This is an open-slotted culvert, like

Burpee Millstream. Fernmount, Sunbury County, New Brunswick. Is abandoned for lack of traffic. Note: rounded portals.

a cattle grid, meant to carry rainwater and melted snow away from the vulnerable lintel.

The quirk of an individual builder occurs on a couple of New Brunswick bridges, and at least one in Quebec. This is a small roof over the lower abutment to fend off the drip from the eaves. This could not have been a serious or widespread problem.

Occasional grace-notes were applied at portals, such as extra moulding or a curved bit of wood as a decorative touch.

Finally, one peculiarity. Under the eaves of many New Brunswick

Burnside, Hayne. Keswick River, York County, New Brunswick. Unusual small roof protects log abutments from eaves drip.

Mangrumbridge, Becaguimec River, Carleton County, New Brunswick. Note: square holes at eaves for temporary scaffolding used during roof repairs.

bridges are mystifying square holes at regular intervals. Sometimes these are boarded over. Their purpose? Simply to support a temporary scaffolding when the roof needs repairs.

IV

Enemies of
the Covered Bridge

IN ANSWER to a protest over demolition of a covered bridge in Fundy
National Park in 1950, a chief Bridge Engineer wrote: "We have a large
number of covered bridges in New Brunswick; in fact, eight miles of
the same, with a total of 307 on record. Many of these were built in 1898
and are still functioning. They have been most economical, requiring
very little maintenance; constructed from our own native timber;
framed and erected by native workmen. They are gradually being
replaced by more up-to-date structures."

Two hundred covered bridges have gone in the quarter century since
that was written, so it might seem that the N.B. Department of Highways
(Le Ministère de la Voirie) was bent on their wholesale demolition.
Still, 107 remain, the greatest concentration in the world. The province
requires 10,000 highway bridges to cross its numerous lakes and rivers.

Wood Mills. Canadian Armed Forces Base Gagetown, Sunbury County, New Brunswick. Partially restored.

And New Brunswick may claim great variety in its covered bridges—several pairs of "twins", bridges with steel intersections, e.g. the Narrows and Florenceville; bridges over tidal waters, e.g. Vaughan Creek #1 and #2, Saint John County; the longest, the (1282-foot Hartland, Carleton County); the shortest (56 foot Quisibis, Madawaska County).

Records of covered bridges were not kept with exactitude because so many of them were privately built or owned. Quebec estimates that it had 1000 at the beginning of this century. Its most recent publication tallies only 130, and many of these have disappeared since the list was compiled. A count early in 1975 indicated 80-some at most, the remainder victims of progress, weather and vandals. Truck drivers would like to see the roads straightened and all the narrow covered bridges replaced with wide concrete bridges.

Eel River #2. Eel River, York County, New Brunswick. Traffic no longer
justifies costly repairwork.

Covered bridge enthusiasts would gladly see every example preserved.
They view the picturesque structures as living, useful examples of
the pioneer arts and the sturdy craftsmanship of the grassroots, and
examples of rustic charm. (In our nostalgia for the slower more serene
way of life, we may well attribute exaggerated virtues to our forefathers.)
To visitors from other provinces or lands where no covered bridge
remains or ever existed, these structures spanning pretty streams or
broad rivers are a delight.

Cherishing antiques, hanging on to outmoded items, is an expensive luxury. No area can afford to clutter its progress with every relic of the past. Yet in some places and at some times, there has been a wholesale clearing away of historic structures, to make way for the sterile modern forms. It is a never-ending debate, of course. Is the upkeep of a covered bridge justified on grounds other than as a quaint tourist attraction? Is the interest great enough to justify the average $50,000 required in 1975 to rebuild an aged bridge?

It calls for a neat balancing act on the part of New Brunswick's Department of Highways and its Tourist Development Branch, and of Quebec's Ministère des Transports and its Direction Générale du Tourisme.

"The government is spending all its money keeping up the old wrecks," growls the motorist, who unexpectedly drops into a pothole. "They oughta tear them all down and put in concrete bridges. After they fill this hole!"

Much as the highway engineers would like to keep all the rate-payers happy, they must consider all claims, and look at the situation realistically.

"First of all," explained one engineer, "we don't need so many bridges nowadays, because we no longer plod at horses' pace. What's another mile or two in a car?"

Thus it is not essential to maintain every bridge. For instance, there was a covered bridge about every mile along the Napan River near Chatham, Northumberland County, N.B. Today only one tattered derelict stands, closed to traffic.

So they repair the bridges that are in constant use, lay scabbing over the deck, re-side, re-roof, prop them up with new pilings, put in new planks, crossbeams and stringers. The lichened, sagging covered bridge on a little-used tote road in the bush, such as Eel River #2, York County, is necessarily neglected, left to the destruction of porcupines and bark beetles, and the crushing weight of winter snows.

Piers and abutments on logging rivers suffer the battering of logs hurtling downstream to saw or pulp-mills. River drives in New

Coulonge. Coulonge River near Fort Coulonge, Pontiac County, Quebec. Note: stepped-back portals.

Brunswick are a thing of the past, and logs are hauled across the bridges by truck. In Quebec log drives continue in many rivers, and the logs still jam up under the covered bridges of the Gatineau.

Though legal weight limits are clearly posted on both portals (limiting loads, for example, to 12 tons or 11 tonnes), occasional weight checks prove that logging trucks are generally overloaded, sometimes carrying 50 tons where 10 tons is the legal limit. Truckers know that the carrying capacity is greater than "the working load figure".

The highway engineer was not unsympathetic. "There's nothing vicious about their overloading. The trucker is paid by the tons he delivers, so that economically, he must take as much as possible on each trip. For the same reason, he's apt to drive too fast, and hit the bridge with an impact undreamt of when the bridges were built.

"Often drivers are careless, and don't slow down enough for the

Grand Remous. Rivière du Diable, Gatineau County, Quebec. Note: two spans. This bridge has scabbing on deck, trap door and ladder to reach rocks below. Steel arches at both portals.

turn on to the bridge. So they ram the portal, or smash the overhead beams with loads stacked too high. Naturally, they curse the confining bridge rather than their own driving."

In fact, when the driver of an overloaded truck crashes through the decking, his first act may be to rip down the load limit sign, then argue it hadn't been there to warn him.

Farmers, too, become impatient with the covered bridges. The Drouin bridge over the Coaticook River, Stanstead County, Que., is frequently threatened by farmers who are just waiting for its sagging timbers to collapse into the river. "We'll never get a decent bridge until it's gone," they mutter.

Arson is a problem in both Quebec and New Brunswick. The St. Canut bridge, Deux Montagnes County, was deliberately burned in 1973 "by a maniac from the next parish."

More widespread is the destruction on Hallowe'en. Lonely bridges and deserted farmhouses are the favourite targets for youthful arsonists. On this unholy night, the Royal Canadian Mounted Police in New Brunswick and Quebec's Sécurité Provinciale patrol with special vigilance, and even lend surplus walkie-talkie sets to the highway

Beaufort. Southwest Branch of Miramichi River, Carleton County, New Brunswick.
Note: unusually high gable and white paint at portals, diagonal planking.

engineers. "We're out on the roads for the whole night," said the
engineer, "trying to protect our wooden bridges and other buildings."

Despite such vigilance, the fires are not all caught and extinguished
in time. Three of New Brunswick's longer spans went up in smoke in
1974. Impatient truckers were suspected, but to get a conviction the
arsonist must be taken in the act.

Some vandalism is the result of pure laziness. It's easier for a hunter
or fisherman to rip a few dried boards off the covered bridge than to
hunt a dead tree for his campfire. Mindless boredom is responsible for
other wilful damage. A thoughtless boy finds idle amusement in kicking
and kicking at a board until it is loosened and falls with a splash into
the river below.

Some destruction is selfish, as when a thief steals the weathered
siding to line a recreation room for rustic effect.

In truth, the regional engineers of the province weary in well-doing
in their efforts to preserve the covered bridges. "We just repaired that

MacFarlane. East Branch of Turtle Creek, Albert County, New Brunswick.
It has had considerable repairwork and is now used illegally as a garbage dump.

bridge two months ago," said one road foreman, "Then last week, a
too-high load came and ripped the end out of 'er."

Similarly a drunken driver, or prankster, raised the boom of his
pulploader when going through the bridge over the Tynemouth Creek,
Saint John County. This ripped one portal out.

Despite the protection offered by the roofing and siding, the wooden
bridges do wear out. The compression and tension factors weaken, the
bridge sags, or the planking rots. Rain finds its way into joints, frost
heaves piers, moving water nibbles at piers and abutments, and spring
freshets with their ice cakes and tree snags do their share of damage.

Complaints about ice destruction are nothing new. The Journals
of the New Brunswick House of Assembly repeat time after time, that
bridges were carried out by ice or damaged severely. One Commissioner
grumbled testily in 1840, "There was more injury done at Earl's Creek

57

Silver Hill or Salmon Hole. Hammond River, Kings County, New Brunswick. "At times salmon were so very plentiful that you could virtually cross over on their backs at the shallows." The oldest (dated) bridge in New Brunswick, it was out of service for several years before being replaced in 1975. Note: unusually high log abutments and "scabbing" of deck.

bridge last Fall in one week after having been frozen and a severe thaw coming than by the whole summer's travelling."

One wonders how long the five rock-and-log cribs under the 815-foot Upper Dorchester bridge, Westmorland County, can withstand the twice-a-day battle between the strong current of the Memramcook River and the notoriously high tides of the Bay of Fundy. Termed "the prettiest bridge in Eastern Canada", it is the second longest covered bridge in New Brunswick, and possibly in the world. It has been closed to vehicular traffic for several years.

New Brunswick's Department of Highways list of covered bridges telescopes the dramatic tale of destruction into a single word or brief phrase. "Collapsed" indicates weary timbers; "Washed out" and "Destroyed by ice and high water" are frequent notations, as is "Replaced." They tell little of the circumstances, but leave no doubt that another link with our country's past has been broken.

V

Hope for the Future

HAPPILY, there has been an awakening and change of attitude.
Today, old covered bridges do not necessarily disappear. In New
Brunswick's list the old term "abandoned" is now often replaced by the
phrase "out of service." Old bridges are not automatically torn down
when a new highway is built. Some serve to shelter road equipment or
farm machinery while the bridge's future is being decided.

If the old site is required for a new bridge, the covered bridge may
be shifted up- or downstream, still useful for foot traffic. This has
happened to perhaps a dozen bridges in Quebec and New Brunswick.

A notable example is the large Moosehorn Brook bridge, Kings
County, N.B., preserved to everyone's satisfaction on a loop of the old
road. The covered bridge sits in a pretty little park, while its concrete
successor carries the heavy traffic a couple hundred yards downstream.

Moosehorn Brook, Kings County, New Brunswick, was the first covered bridge in the province to be restored as the focal point of a small picnic park between old and new roads. The covered bridges present problems to over-size house trailers too.

A most dramatic shifting of a covered bridge took place about 1973 near the Quebec–Vermont border, Brome County. Some 150 feet above Mud Creek (a clear rippling brook) stretched a fine example of a Town truss bridge, still sound in construction, but no longer strong enough for today's traffic demands. The covered bridge rested on two staunch spurs of rock, a site coveted for the abutments of a new bridge. Quebec engineers ingeniously moved the old bridge sideways the width

Mud Creek. Mud Creek near Coaticook, Brome County, Quebec. Two bridges now span the creek high above it. The covered bridge was shifted downstream the width of the new bridge.

Notre Dame de la Providence, Chaudière River near Beauceville, Beauce County, Quebec. At 495 feet it is the longest covered bridge in Quebec, reaching from a farm field to the village park. Its modern replacement is immediately upstream.

of the new road. It must have been a fascinating operation to watch. So now Mud Creek has two bridges 150 feet above it.

Even if a bridge can no longer carry traffic, it and its setting may take a new lease on life in the form of a roadside park with the bridge as a focal attraction. Such parks are infinitely more attractive than the usual lay-by carved out of the bush with no view or other focus.

Quebec's longest covered bridge spans Rivière Chaudière at Notre Dame de la Providence, Beauce County, near St. Georges. The bridge of four spans was built in 1926 and was torn out by flood waters two years later at midnight of Easter Sunday. Thrown up on the fields it seemed a complete wreck, but local workmen forged ahead and had it back in service by autumn. It served traffic until November, 1970, when the new large concrete bridge a few yards upstream was opened.

Ste. Catherine. Misseau Creek near Ayer's Cliff, Stanstead County, Quebec. The bridge is the focal point of a small park at the junction of two main routes.

The old bridge no longer carries traffic though it still spans the Chaudière, extending from the town's picnic grounds to a farmer's field.

A similar happy fate overtook Ste. Catherine bridge over Misseau Creek, near Ayer's Cliff, Stanstead County. It sits in its old location, now surrounded by a small triangular wayside park at the junction of two major routes, undisturbed by traffic.

Occasional covered bridges remain in their original locations, simply because the traffic is so light, perhaps to a single farm beyond, as at Cookshire in Compton County over the Eaton River. Milby bridge, over the Moe River east of Lennoxville, Sherbrooke County, leads only to a trailer parking lot and is a picturesque example of a Town lattice with large tree-knees supporting the roof.

Preserving a covered bridge presents its own legal problems. Who owns the bridge when the N.B. Department of Highways or Le Ministère des Transports du Québec gives it up? To what body should the ownership deed be transferred? Who is responsible if an accident occurs there?

When the Stanbridge Historical Society, which maintains a fine small museum in Stanbridge, Stanstead County, heard that the covered bridge in Stanbridge East was doomed, they moved into action to "conserve" it. The old wooden bridge was moved along the Rivière aux Brochets, just downstream of its concrete replacement.

The towns and hamlets of New Brunswick are liberally dotted with historical societies and farm organizations, both taking a keen interest in the local scene. But at present, there is no covered bridge association such as exists in many parts of the United States. Until recently, the various local organizations have taken the covered bridges for granted as part of the scenery, perhaps deplored the demolition of a familiar structure, perhaps recorded its origin, but little more.

In 1972, the League for Rural Renewal was launched by a very distinguished New Brunswicker. Brigadier the Honourable Milton Gregg of Fredericton, now retired after a long career of public service in army, politics, and diplomacy, heads the League. He and others found the quality of life changing too much. They were not against progress, but felt that it should not be at the cost of ruining the countryside or changing its people unduly.

The League for Rural Renewal links with the efforts of the Heritage Trust and other groups in attempting to preserve the finest aspects of the past. It is remarkable for having no membership fees, no elections, no staff, no office and only one meeting a year. Business and committee work is done largely by telephone to avoid paperwork.

Brigadier-General Gregg functions as president, and Mr. Hugh John Fleming, a former provincial premier, is the equally casually appointed vice-president. Both display plenty of energy and enthusiasm and no tendency to dwell on "the good old days". Robert Tweedie, long associated with the Tourist Development Branch, took on the unexacting chore of treasurer. Don Williams of Durham Bridge, N.B., acted as liaison between these co-ordinators and the rural leaders. This was highly important, for the retired rural cooperators were glad to work at projects that would aid their communities, but their aims were accomplished through encouragement, not by issuing orders. And hence it works.

Only retired citizens were sought as members. People who love the New Brunswick countryside and want the rural values preserved, and who are willing to serve free, without expecting any material rewards. However, the League welcomes "participants" of any age who wish to support the program.

Some charter members were deeply concerned about the rapid loss of covered bridges. They sought some way to encourage local groups to preserve the covered bridges in their areas by having those that were abandoned fixed up as the centres for little picnic parks.

The key word is "encourage". The League stimulates local initiative for the bridge-park projects, and provides free technical services to aid local groups which provide voluntary labour and material for their "community bridge park". A small federal grant is stretched to an astonishing degree to encourage the renovation, to their rustic appearance, of as many as possible of the bridges.

The bridge-park idea became a primary concern. To promote the idea, local interest must be aroused. Then local groups must be found that are willing to take on responsibility. Such protection worked remarkably well in one instance when the "abandoned" Sawmill Creek covered bridge in Albert County, was in danger one spring night.

A motorist speeded into Riverside to a member of the League shouting, "Your covered bridge is on fire!" Friends rushed to the scene with brooms and blankets, and soon beat out a grass fire which some boys had set too close to the weathered old structure.

Less happily, when the federal government in Ottawa decided to create Kouchibouguac National Park on New Brunswick's eastern coast, Parks authorities failed to pave the way adequately. Some disgruntled inhabitants of the area retaliated against expropriation by burning a showpiece covered bridge, and later also the timbers imported for re-building it.

Eight small picnic parks had been opened by the end of 1975 "with

65

"The shortest covered bridge in the world" attracts tourists to a motel near Edmundston, Madawaska County, New Brunswick.

another fourteen in the works," Brigadier-General Gregg could report gleefully. Some of the latter will centre around covered bridges destined for replacement. By request, they were demolished by the Armed Forces as a military exercise, and the timbers are stored for future re-erection somewhere else.

Incidentally, there is considerable demand from private contractors for the long stout timbers of demolished covered bridges, but generally these are stored by the Department of Highways for use in bridge repairs.

The present eight bridge-parks include three in Sunbury County—Hoyt, Smye at Mill Settlement, and Rusagonis. The two-span bridge

Russell Owen. Rusagonis River, Sunbury County, New Brunswick.

with unusual window-lighting was built at Upper Rusagonis in 1909.
The Department of Highways labels it "#592 North Rusagonis River"
but local people prefer the old name "Russell Owen Bridge" in honour
of a long-gone farmer, whose land lay close to the bridge. At the east
end of the bridge is the little park and a pioneer cemetery. At the west end
is a grey shingled farmhouse that was originally a posthouse on
the Fredericton–St. Stephens stagecoach run. It has a fireplace in
every room.

Rusagonis Covered Bridge Park was the first to get under way, and
is a prime example of how a small community got behind the project.
The farmer at the east end of the bridge donated land beside the river
for a park area, a bit of waste land where people had dumped old
machinery. The debris was covered up with some two hundred loads of
earth, free, because the Department of Highways was ditching nearby,
and this proved a convenient place to dump. The local committee
acquired forty loads of gravel, the bargain price of $10.00 a load,
and hired a bulldozer to spread it.

Hayseed from another farmer's barn was spread thickly, and green grass sprouted in two weeks' time. Yet another farmer donated space in his barn to house the picnic tables and barbecues in winter. Fence posts came from crown lands, with the blessing of the New Brunswick Department of Forestry. The splendid story of rural cooperation brought photographers, and the Russell Owen bridge appeared in "living colour" in tourist advertising in international magazines.

Should there be swings and teeter-totters for children? The local committee debated the issue. The decision was to place these in the village playground, rather than on the picnic park where joyous shrieks might disturb adult picnickers.

When a group of young people asked permission to hold a corn roast in the bridge park, this called for deliberation. Would they need supervision? The committee bravely granted permission and determined to stay off the scene, resigning themselves to cleaning-up the next day. To the astonishment and pride of the work squad, the young people had tidied up completely — not so much as a cigarette butt lay around.

Although the League for Rural Renewal accepts as members only retired people, it welcomes cooperation from people of all ages. For example, the efforts of a group of 4-H youngsters were valuable in creating the picnic park at the old Smye Bridge, Oromocto #2. The western approach to the old ford and the bridge is low and was overgrown with shrubs and small trees. The young people bushwacked out the area, making space for picnic tables.

Local committees now take their covered bridges seriously. When this same Oromocto bridge needed a new roof, the Department of Highways budgeted for aluminum sheeting. A loud protest arose. This was not restoration! Since cedar shingles cost twice as much, the committee passed the hat, and made up the difference. The old Smye bridge has a new shingled roof, historically accurate and more aesthetically pleasing.

There was no such group to defend the Bell bridge downstream, South Oromocto #3, whose aluminum roof dazzles the eye.

The covered bridges of Quebec and New Brunswick have long attracted individual members of the American covered bridge associations

68

Bell. South branch of Oromocto River, Sunbury County, New Brunswick. Repairs include new sheeting and aluminum roof.

who have left their calling cards discreetly tacked up in the bridges they visited.

News of the League's projects brought an unusual development in 1973. The National Society for the Preservation of Covered Bridges, a a federation of many state associations, launched a safari to visit as many of New Brunswick bridges as they could crowd into nine days. The route was lined up carefully in advance with the assistance of the Department of Highways, the League, and with the cooperation of many local organizations.

"It was a tight schedule," liaison man Don Williams admitted. "Up and away by 8 o'clock in the morning, and often not back to their motel until 9 o'clock at night. Then they had to write up their notes or whatever. Hardly in bed when out again. It was like the army—roll in, roll over, roll out."

The procession of twenty trekkers in a dozen cars visited forty

Southwest Otnabog. Canadian Armed Forces Base Gagetown, Sunbury County, New Brunswick.

covered bridges in the counties of Albert, Kings, Queens and Sunbury, and managed to fit in local hospitality as well. The highlight for them was when the Canadian Armed Forces helicoptered high tea to the group when they visited the two covered bridges still surviving at Base Gagetown, which had been rehabilitated as part of a training program. In all, the concensus was, "the best safari ever!"

It was a splendid introduction to "The picture Province". A second safari in 1974 concentrated on the bridges on the western side of the province.

Both safaris were a thrill to the visitors, and an eye-opener to those New Brunswickers who had not previously recognized their historic treasures. They were impressed with the knowledgeable interest displayed by the visitors, and marvelled at the difficulties they overcame to get unusual photographs.

Florenceville bridge. Saint John River, Carleton County, New Brunswick. Has five steel spans and one covered wooden span, an unusual combination.

You don't need a group or a conducted tour to visit the covered bridges of Quebec and New Brunswick. Using the lists in this book, mark the location of the bridges on the largest-scale map you can acquire . . . and still be prepared to ask directions often.

As an example, you could track down the covered bridges of the Magaguadavic (pronounced Magadavy) River, starting in St. George, where the river hurtles down in a spectacular waterfall in the centre of a charming town. Track the river upstream, and you'll find four covered bridges not far apart. There are another five on the Digideguash (often called Diggity) River, three more on the Hammond, and two on Vaughn Creek in St. Martin's.

71

Macamic, Abitibi County, Quebec. Department of Highways workers repair bridge damaged by an over-large truck.

Take binoculars and a bird book (birds love the covered bridge sites). You will never hear more caroling, chirping, fluting and twittering.

You could track down covered bridges close to the Saint John River valley, or in the highlands of the interior where the best potatoes grow. Sussex could be the focal point for your explorations in Kings County. Quebec covered bridges are more widely dispersed, though there are more than a dozen in the Eastern Townships. Another concentration is in the Laurentians, north of Ottawa, two of them on the Gatineau River.

Gardner's Creek. Gardner's Creek where it enters the tidal Bay of Fundy, Saint John County, New Brunswick.

As New Englanders led the way in designing covered bridges, their descendants have demonstrated many uses for the bridge motif on china, cloth and wallpaper, place mats, paintings, wall hangings, note-paper, and tie-clips. The covered bridge theme has been competently exploited in books, pamphlets and postcards in areas with far fewer covered bridges than Quebec or New Brunswick. Has anyone patented a toy wooden bridge a child could put together?

VI

Covered Bridges
in Ontario

ONTARIO, like Quebec and New Brunswick, had many rivers that needed bridging. Like them, it had extensive forests of hardwood and pine, but it had little usable cedar for shingles. Is that the reason Ontario showed so little enthusiasm for roofing its bridges?

A search through Provincial Archives reveals few photographs or sketches of covered bridges. At best, it appears there were only seven enclosed bridges in the province. The one at West Montrose, Waterloo County, about 12 miles northwest of Kitchener, is the sole survivor, spending its days in semi-retirement as a historic landmark and tourist attraction.

The other bridges were located at Napanee, a Town lattice built about 1840; at Peterborough, a two-span bridge over the Otonabee River; at Frankford, a two-span over the Trent; at Trenton, the outlet of the Trent Canal System, a six-span bridge with an unusual feature in that one span could be lifted to allow sailboats to pass underneath; and two covered bridges over the Black River (Rivière aux Raisins) at Williamstown and Martintown, in Glengarry County.

The Martintown covered bridge replaced the original open structure when that was swept away in a flood in 1861 or 62. A tree swept down the raging river and caused a jam, forcing the river to find a new course around the main stream, and the bridge gave way. The covered bridge was built the same year by the Sylvesters, who used the rare Haupt truss, invented by Herman Haupt of Pennsylvania.

The town fathers economically re-cycled the old timbers to build a suburban bridge.

The trusses of the new covered bridge were fastened with wooden pins and there was a low dividing wall 4 inches thick and 5 inches above the floor creating a two-lane deckway. Evidently it was a good design for it stood for over a century and was replaced only in 1963 by a concrete structure. The bridge bore the traditional signs at each portal "Any person or persons passing through this bridge faster than a walk will be prosecuted according to law".

The bridge was not lighted at first, an old-timer recalled. "On one Hallowe'en night, a milk wagon was perched on top of the bridge. I remember seeing it next morning." Perhaps that is why a large gasoline lantern was installed. It was let down every night and hauled up again by rope the next day.

If Ontario built half a dozen covered bridges, why not more?

J. D. Millar, Deputy Minister of Highways, in 1949, jotted down a number of probable reasons. The pioneers were farm folk not given to much travel or road-building. When they did make a journey it was usually by boat using the Great Lakes, or the Trent or Rideau Canal Systems, or they travelled in winter over the numerous frozen swamps and the frozen lakes. Sleighs were plentiful, wagons scarce.

Probably the main reason was that Ontario's early settlers, coming from France and the British Isles, were used to building stone bridges, which did not need housing. And the English military, who built pioneer roads, preferred unobstructed vertical clearance.

West Montrose. Waterloo County, Ontario. East side and south portal, winter 1975.

The railway-building era overlapped that of water transportation, and steel and concrete quickly replaced wood for bridge building.

Nearly a century old, the West Montrose bridge still spans the long winding Grand River, which in spate is a ravening monster, swirling along, tearing out trees, piling up ice cakes, spilling over its banks to a width of half a mile. Each spring the south approach was flooded, but now various dams control its rampage so that there's scarcely enough water under the bridge in mid-summer for a boy to skinny-dip. But there is plenty to form ice in winter, and kids still clear off rink space for hockey. They have to watch out for snowmobiles coursing over the snowy ice.

The province of Ontario, energetic, prosperous and determined to keep abreast of its neighbour to the south, has often been ruthless in weeding out the past, viewing old structures as signs of decadence, suitable only for demolition.

The final surviving covered bridge at West Montrose was destined for that fate, but public protest reprieved it. When the demolition crew examined it closely in 1942 they found the bridge in surprisingly good condition. The timbers were too big and sound to be easily demolished. The bridge would not take today's heavy loads, but it still served a useful purpose for the democrats and buggies of the Mennonites on their way to meeting or market.

Engineers of the Department of Highways studied the area that year and were critical of the siting of the bridge. "There is a sharp turn and a rather steep grade in the South approach, and another turn in the road (a blind corner) some 300 yards from the North end. There are also several bad curves and corners within a couple of miles of the bridge in both directions." These presented no problem back in 1881 when the road was laid out for the benefit of horse-drawn vehicles.

The covered bridge at West Montrose was built for Woolwich Township, Waterloo County, by the Bear (or Baer) brothers Sam and John in 1881, at a cost of $3179.50. The finest pine timbers some of them 9″ × 18″ × 50′ were cut and hauled from Doon. Their finished bridge measured 196.5 feet across the Grand River with an additional 6-foot overhang at each portal. The bridge was 17 feet wide inside with a 13-foot clearance, and consisted of two equal spans resting on cedar cribs, now replaced by concrete wing abutments and a stone centre pier. The louvered window openings admitted air and light while keeping out snow and rain. The 3-inch oak planking was laid transversely and not nailed down.

"Those loose planks could be heard rattling a mile off," recalled the late Albert Devitt, a venerable local historian.

By 1933 the skilled workmanship of the Bear brothers showed signs of age. In spite of sheeting outside and to a height of 5 feet inside, moisture had rotted part of a lower chord. A "needlebeam" was replaced, and the timber chord spliced with steel plates.

At some time in its history the centre pier was undermined by the rush of river water, so that its east corner of the south span or upstream end was noticeably tilted.

Responsibility for the West Montrose bridge was taken over from the County of Waterloo in 1937 by the Ontario Department of Highways. Promptly came the demand for a new bridge.

The engineers recommended a re-routing of Highway #86 and a new big bridge over the Grand River.

Instead, a 2-ton load limit and 10-mile speed limit were imposed on the elderly bridge, but both were regularly exceeded. Among the dusty rafters was stored the old sign "Anyone driving a horse-drawn vehicle through this bridge faster than a walk is liable to the full punishment of the law".

A school bus with 55 students aboard weighed more than 13 tons and crossed twice daily for years. It carried high school students to the Elmira district high school. Finally the school principal began insisting that the students evacuate the bus at the entrance to the bridge and walk across the bridge to re-board at the other end, a move loudly protested by the students twice a day. "It's not that we want the old bridge removed," the principal declared. "We just want a safer one. Perhaps the old bridge could be preserved."

Among those students was Lloyd Hartwick. The Hartwick family, living in a snug stone house at the south end of the bridge, has been intimately connected with the covered bridge at West Montrose. Gus Hartwick was a patrolman with the Department of Highways, and one of his duties was to "snow" the bridge in winter for the benefit of sleighs and cutters. This is no longer necessary since the Mennonites now use buggies year round because the roads are now cleared of snow in winter.

Mrs. Gus Hartwick took on the chore of lighting the bridge for a couple of years before turning the job over to her 13-year old son. Every day at dusk, Lloyd cleaned the glass chimneys of two lanterns, poured in the kerosene at home. Then he stepped across the gravel road to the bridge, a lighted lantern swinging from each hand. From a corner of the bridge he took a long pole with a hook at the end. He hoisted one lantern to a hook on a sturdy beam, 13 feet above the bridge deck, at the south end of the bridge where there were (and are) both a sharp curve and a grade; the other lantern was hung about two-thirds of the way through. In winter Lloyd had to hang the lanterns out immediately after school. But in summer's long twilight they didn't have to go up

Lloyd Hartwick, 15, ready to hoist a lighted lantern to a hook in the rafters. His home is across the road behind him. 1949.

until after 9 o'clock. The lantern-boy was paid $4.00 a month.

Lloyd Hartwick's job ended in 1950, when the Department of Highways overhauled the old bridge and installed electricity. The floor was replaced with a laminated deck of two-by-fours, and covered with asphalt bonded with crushed stone to form a smooth hard surface. The approaches were brought up to grade and the centre pier bearing was rebuilt. Otherwise the bridge is much in its original state.

It is alleged that Henry Ford wished to add it to his famous collection of Americana at Fort Dearborn, Greenfield, Michigan, but for some reason the deal fell through.

Perhaps this reason was an awakened awareness of the historic value of the unique old structure. By 1950 the Department of Highways realized that the bridge was quite irreplaceable in modern times. So much interest in the covered bridge was shown that the Department of Highways became nervous of fire.

"Due to the fire hazard which might result from a lantern being blown down or knocked down by high loaded vehicles, it was decided to illuminate the bridge by electricity," wrote J. D. Millar, Deputy Minister of Highways. "I am frank to admit electric illumination is out of keeping with the character of the bridge, but necessary if the bridge is to be protected from fire."

But the three 100-watt bulbs are set in the old lanterns as a reminder of the lantern-boy's duties .

By 1955 Highway #86 was re-routed a couple of miles north of the old road and West Montrose village. A large concrete bridge spanned the Grand River several hundred yards upstream from the covered wooden bridge.

Again the historic bridge was in danger of demolition, but sentiment aroused by an Old-Timers Association again reprieved the death sentence.

Normally, the old bridge would have reverted to the original owner, the Township of Woolwich, but the provincial government cheerfully assumed the responsibility for it because of its immense interest.

It is claimed that the old-fashioned covered bridge at West Montrose is the most photographed and sketched bridge in the province, bar none.

BRIDGE LOCATIONS IN QUEBEC*

MUNICIPALITY/WATERCOURSE	LOCATION/NEAREST HIGHWAY(S)	LENGTH OF BRIDGE (in metres)
ABITIBI COUNTY		
Amos-Est/Harricana	8 km west of Saint-Maurice/109, 395	65.5
Amos-Est/Panache	7.2 km northwest of Saint-Maurice/109, 395	26.8
Laas/Lavigne	4.8 km northwest of Langlois/397	—
La Morendière/Laflamme	4 km southeast of La Morendière/397	34.1
La Morendière/Laflamme	4 km west of Rochebaucourt/397	36.3
Rochebaucourt/Laflamme	4 km northeast of Rochebaucourt/397	63.4
Rochebaucourt/Tourville	12 km southeast of Rochebaucourt/397	39.3
Senneville/Bourlamaque	0.8 km east of Val-Senneville/397	43.9
Senneville/Senneville	2.4 km north of Val Senneville/397	31.7
Trécesson/Villemontel	8.8 km northeast of Manneville/395	36.3
Vassan/Vassan	2.4 km south of Vassan/111	32
Authier/Bellefeuille	0.8 km east of Authier/111	21.9
Clermont/Desmeloizes	6.4 km west of Saint-Vital/111, 393	32
Clerval/Lac Abitibi	20.1 km south of Clerval/393	49.4
Colombourg/La Sarre	2.4 km east of Sainte-Hélène/393	80.8
La Sarre/Desmeloizes	3.2 km northwest of La Sarre/111	35.7
La Sarre/Bouchard	5.6 km northwest of La Sarre/111	22.6
Launay/Villemontel	3.2 km southeast of Launay-Station/111	51.2
Rousseau/Leslie	0.8 km southeast of Saint-Ephrem/111	24.4
Rousseau/Turgeon	4 km east of Beaucanton/111	44.2
Rousseau/Turgeon	4.8 km southeast of Villebois/393	29
Saint-Janvier/Lois	0.8 km east of Macamic/111	33.2
Saint-Janvier/Macamic	15.3 km northwest of Saint-Mathias/111	39.6
Saint-Janvier/La Sarre	9.6 km southeast of Saint-Janvier/111	62.2
Taschereau/Bellefeuille	2.4 km west of Taschereau/111	25.9
Taschereau/Bellefeuille	3.2 km west of Taschereau/111	24.7
ARTHABASKA COUNTY		
Warwick/Des Pins	1.6 km west of Warwick/116	29.6
BEAUCE COUNTY		
Notre-Dame-de-la-Providence/Chaudière	0.8 km west of Notre-Dame-des-Pins/173	154.5
Sainte-Clothilde/Dupuis	4.8 km east of Sainte-Clothilde/108	22.3
Saint-Victor-de-Tring/Saint-Victor	1.6 km west of Saint-Victor/108	29.6
BERTHIER COUNTY		
Sainte-Geneviève-de-Berthier/Bayonne	Northwest of Berthierville/158	33.5
BONAVENTURE COUNTY		
New Richmond/Petite Cascapédia	14.5 km from Saint-Edgar/132	89.3
New Richmond/Petite Cascapédia	Near New Richmond/132	111.9
Port-Daniel-Est/Port-Daniel	4.8 km north of Port-Daniel/132	25.6
BROME COUNTY		
Adamsville/Yamaska	4.8 km west of Adamsville/139	26.8
Adamsville/Yamaska	1.6 km north of Adamsville/139	32
Potton/Mud Creek	4.8 km southeast of Highwater/243	30.8
Potton/Missisquoi	East of Highwater/243	22.6

*Information from *Ponts couverts au Québec*, Direction Générale du Tourisme, Québec, 1976.

MUNICIPALITY/WATERCOURSE	LOCATION/NEAREST HIGHWAY(S)	LENGTH OF BRIDGE (in metres)
CHAMPLAIN COUNTY		
Saint-Séverin/Des Envies	3.2 km west of Saint-Séverin/159	33.5
	4.8 km west of Saint-Séverin/153	
CHICOUTIMI COUNTY		
Boileau/Des Ha! Ha!	South of Sainte-Bernadette/381	36.9
Saint-Jean/Saint-Jean	6.4 km northeast of Anse-Saint-Jean/170	37.2
COMPTON COUNTY		
Cookshire/Eaton	1.6 km north of Cookshire/253	40.5
Eaton/North	4.8 km northeast of Eaton/253	34.1
Tingwick/Au Saumon	1.6 km north of Gould/108, 257	62.8
Saint-Isidore/Eaton	12 km southwest of Saint-Mathias/253	29.3
GASPÉ-EST COUNTY		
Grande-Vallée/Grande Vallée	Near Grande-Vallée/132	43.9
GATINEAU COUNTY		
Egan-Sud/Désert	11.3 km northwest of Maniwaki/105	39
Wakefield/Gatineau	1.6 km east of Wakefield/105	87.8
HUNTINGDON COUNTY		
Elgin/Châteauguay	9.6 km from Powerscourt/202	55.2
JOLIETTE COUNTY		
Saint-Côme/L'Assomption	4.8 km northwest of Saint-Côme/343	29
KAMOURASKA COUNTY		
Saint-Onésime/Ouelle	11.3 km northeast of Saint-Onésime/132	36.6
Saint-Onésime/Ouelle	10.5 km southeast of Saint-Onésime/132	21.3
LABELLE COUNTY		
Chute-Saint-Philippe/Kiamika	16 km from Chute-Saint-Philippe/117, 311	39.6
Chute-Saint-Philippe/Kiamika	14.5 km southwest of Chute-Saint-Philippe/117,311	34.4
Lac-des-Écorces/Kiamika	12.9 km west of Val-Barette/117	29.3
La Macaza/Macaza	11.3 km from La Macaza/117	39
Saint-Aimé/Du Lièvre	6.4 km west of Kiamika/309	76.8
Saint-Aimé/Du Lièvre	6.4 km west of Kiamika/309	46.3
Saint-Aimé/Du Lac-des-Îles	1.6 km east of Lac-des-Îles/309	32.3
LAVIOLETTE COUNTY		
Bourgeois/Bostonnais	Northeast of Saint-Jean-Bosco/155	41.5
Bourgeois/Bostonnais	0.8 km east of Saint-Jean-Bosco/155	41.8
Langelier/La Croche	16 km from La Croche/155	68.3
LÉVIS COUNTY		
Saint-Étienne/Beaurivage	0.8 km northeast of Saint-Agapit/116	38.1
L'ISLET COUNTY		
Saint-Adalbert/Gr. Noire	5.6 km north of Saint-Adalbert/204	38.1
Saint-Pamphile/Saint-Roch	4.8 km northeast of Saint-Pamphile/204	32

MUNICIPALITY/WATERCOURSE	LOCATION/NEAREST HIGHWAY(S)	LENGTH OF BRIDGE (in metres)
MASKINONGÉ COUNTY		
Sainte-Ursule/Maskinongé	0.8 km southeast of Saint-Édouard/348	35.4
MATANE COUNTY		
Les Boules/Tartigou	14.5 km southeast of Les Boules/132	26.8
Saint-Jérôme/Matane	South of Matane/195	45.1
Saint-Jérôme/Matane	West of Saint-René/195	54.3
Saint-Luc/Matane	West of Saint-René/195	44.5
Saint-René/Matane	Near Saint-René/195	51.8
Saint-Ulric/Blanche	3.2 km southeast of Saint-Ulric/132	24.7
MATAPÉDIA COUNTY		
Assemetquagan/Matapédia	Near Routhierville/132	78.6
Saint-Benoît/Matapédia	1.6 km northwest of Amqui/132	44.5
Saint-Jacques/Matapédia	South of Causapscal/132	39.3
Saint-Jacques/Matapédia	South of Causapscal/132	39.6
Sainte-Jeanne-d'Arc/Mistigousche	12.9 km southwest of Sainte-Jeanne-d'Arc/132	24.7
Saint-Léon-le-Grand/Humqui	West of Saint-Léon-le-Grand/195	26.2
MÉGANTIC COUNTY		
Nelson/Palmer	16 km south of Sainte-Agathe/116	39.6
MISSISQUOI COUNTY		
Cowansville/Yamaska	Northwest of Cowansville/139	28.6
Notre-Dame-de-Stanbridge/Aux Brochets	4 km northeast of Pike River/133	41.5
Stanbridge/Aux Brochets	6.4 km south of Stanbridge/202	16.2
Saint-Armand-Ouest/Groat Creek	8 km northwest of Pigeon Hill/202	15.2
MONTMAGNY COUNTY		
Sainte-Lucie/Nord-Ouest	3.2 km northwest of Sainte-Lucie/204	30.5
NICOLET COUNTY		
Bécancourt/Saint-Wenceslas	8 km south of Précieux-Sang/155	29.6
Bécancourt/Saint-Wenceslas	9.6 km south of Précieux-Sang/155	29.6
Saint-Célestin/Saint-Wenceslas	2.4 km southeast of Saint-Célestin/155	24.7
Saint-Joseph/Du Chêne	1.6 km north of Manseau/218	24.4
Saint-Pierre-les-Becquets/Aux Originaux	3.2 km southwest of Sainte-Cécile/218	17.4
PAPINEAU COUNTY		
Bowman/Du Lièvre	1.6 km west of Val-des-Bois/309	132.3
PONTIAC COUNTY		
Mansfield/Coulonge	0.8 km northeast of Fort-Coulonge/148	128.9
RICHMOND COUNTY		
Melbourne/Au Saumon	2.4 km southeast of Melbourne/243	15.8
RIMOUSKI COUNTY		
Duquesne/Petite Rimouski	14.5 km southeast of Saint-Valérien/132	31.7
Mont-Lebel/Neigette	22.5 km northeast of Mont-Lebel/132	28.3
Saint-Anaclet/Neigette	14.5 km east of Neigette/132	29.9
Sainte-Odile/Du Brulé	9.6 km south of Sainte-Odile/132	37.2

MUNICIPALITY/WATERCOURSE	LOCATION/NEAREST HIGHWAY(S)	LENGTH OF BRIDGE (in metres)
LAC ST-JEAN OUEST COUNTY		
Notre-Dame-de-Lorette/Aux Foins	30.6 km from Notre-Dame-de-Lorette/169	27.1
Sainte-Jeanne-d'Arc/Noire	4.8 km north of Sainte-Jeanne-d'Arc/169	25.3
Lac-Bouchette/Ouiatchouan	1.6 km southwest of Lac-Bouchette/155	22.3
SAGUENAY COUNTY		
Pointe-aux-Outardes/Petite-Rivière	12.9 km east of Les Buissons/138	31.7
Sacré-Coeur/Sainte-Marguerite	West of Rivière Sainte-Marguerite/172	39.3
SHERBROOKE COUNTY		
Ascot/Massawippi	0.8 km south of Lennoxville/143	35.1
Ascot/Moe	South of Lennoxville/147	24.1
STANSTEAD COUNTY		
Coaticook/Coaticook	Near Coaticook/147	18.6
Stanstead/Lac Fitch Bay	16 km south of Fitch Bay/141	28
Sainte-Catherine/Misseau	Northwest of Ayer's Cliff/141	19.8
SAINT-MAURICE COUNTY		
Saint-Mathieu/Shawinigan	12.9 km northeast of Saint-Mathieu/153, 351	24.4
TÉMISCAMINGUE COUNTY		
Béarn/Davy	3.2 km southwest of Saint-Dominique/109	39.3
Latulipe & Gaboury/Frazer	4 km south of Latulipe/382	32
TÉMISCOUATA COUNTY		
Saint-Elzéar/Bleue	1.6 km northwest of Rivière-Bleue/289	29.3
TERREBONNE COUNTY		
Saint-Jovite/Du Diable	0.8 km east of Brébeuf/327	44.8
WOLFE COUNTY	1.6 km east of Brébeuf/323	
Saint-Camille/Nicolet, centre	8.8 km northeast of Saint-Camille/255	—

BRIDGE LOCATIONS IN NEW BRUNSWICK*

BRIDGE	YEAR BUILT	LOCATION	LENGTH OF SPAN (in feet)
ALBERT COUNTY			
Bull Creek #1 (Steeves, Harris)	1929	At Salem	86
Chemical Creek #1 (Memel)	1913	Memel Road	164
Coverdale River #2 (Mitton, John)	1925	Road: Salisbury to Colpitts	164
Coverdale River #3 (Colpitts, Bamford)	—	Farm Road to Colpitts, Bamford	87
Coverdale River #7 (Parkindale)	1916	At Parkindale	60
East Turtle Creek #1 (McFarlane)	1907	Osborne Corner at Steeves Mills	170
Lower Forty-five #1 (Fundy National Park)	—	Barrett Road, Fundy National Park	102
Mitton (William)	—	William Mitton Road	87
Point Wolfe	1916	Fundy National Park	95
Pollett River #9 (Riverview)	1908	Church Hill Road	106
Saw Mill Creek #1	—	Road: Hillsboro to Alma	109
Shepody River #1 (Mouth)	1933	Harvey Road	164
Shepody River #3 (Germantown Lake)	1903	Road: Germantown to Midway	60
Turtle Creek #2 (Fillmore)	1912	At Turtle Creek Village	108
Turtle Creek #4 (Peter Jonah)	—	Jonah Road	68
Weldon Creek #3 (Steeves, Hartley)	1923	At Salem	70
CARLETON COUNTY			
Becaguimec River #3 (Mangrum)	1909	Stormdale S.W. ¼ mile	94
Florenceville	1910	Over St. John River at Florenceville (only one span covered)	148
Hartland	1921	At town of Hartland	5 @ 170 2 @ 147
Monquart River #3 (Keenan)	1927	Road: Killowen to Johnsville	86
North Becaguimec River #1 (Adair)	1948	1 mile North of Cloverdale	68
North Becaguimec River #4 (Ellis)	1909	1 mile North of Carlisle	60
North Meduxnekeag River #3 (DeWitt)	1954	Oakville, North to Weston	64
Shikatehawk River #2 (Lockhart Mill)	1954	Road: Bristol to Carlow	64
Shikatehawk River #3	—	Road: Gordonville to Carlow	60
(West Branch) S.W. Miramichi River #8 (Beaufort)	1952	Over St. John River at Florenceville (only one span covered)	148
CHARLOTTE COUNTY			
Canal Covered	1917	Back Road: Canal to Lake Utopia	127
Digdeguash River #2 (Stillwater)	1901	Mill Road	97
Digdeguash River #3 (McGuire)	1915	Roix Road	120
Digdeguash River #4 (McCann)	1938	Pleasant Ridge Road	86
Digdeguash River #5 (Rollingdam)	—	Sorrel Ridge Road	78
Digdeguash River #6 (Dumbarton)	1928	Tryon Settlement Road	78
Linton	1931	Road: St. George to Second Falls	78
Little Lepreau (Mill Pond)	1910	Lepreau Road	106
Magaguadavic River #4 (Second Falls)	1923	Red Rock Road at Second Falls	2 @ 120
Magaguadavic River #7 (Flume Ridge)	1905	Clark's Mill Pond Road	60

*Information from *Covered Bridges of New Brunswick*,
Department of Highways, New Brunswick, 1970.

BRIDGE	YEAR BUILT	LOCATION	LENGTH OF SPAN (in feet)
Maxwell Crossing (Dennis Stream)	1910	Route 3 to David Ridge	63
New River Station	1909	Old Saint John Road	108
Piskahegan	—	Piskahegan Road	63

KENT COUNTY

Buctouche River #4 (Neil Sherwood)	1931	Route 520, two miles east of Route 490	
East St. Nicholas River #1	1925	Six miles west from Rexton on South Branch	75
Graham Creek (Graham, Tom)	1928	Graham Point to Rexton	60
Kouchibouguacis River #5 (Camerons Mill)	1950	Five miles up river from St. Ignace	136
Molus River #1	—	At Bass River Point	132, 126 & 123
St. Nicholas River #1 (North)	1919	Road: Mundleville to Rexton	3 @ 165

KINGS COUNTY

Bell Creek #2 (Marven)	1903	Swamp Road	75
Bloomfield Creek	1917	Bloomfield Station Road	147
Darling's Island	1914	Darling's Island Road	136
Hammond River #2 (French Village)	1922	French Village Road	189
Hammond River #3 (Smithtown)	1914	Damascus Road	189
Kennebecasis River #8 (Salmon)	1899	Smith Creek Road	123
Kennebecasis River #9 (Plumweseep)	1911	Plumweseep Road	78
Meanan Cove	1925	Model Farm to Perry Point	147
Milkish Inlet #1 (Bayswater)	1920	Road: Bayswater to Summerville	2 @ 108
Millstream #5 (Centreville)	1911	Pleasant Ridge Road	98
Smith Creek #1 (Tranton)	1927	Mines Road	128
Smith Creek #5 (Oldfields)	1910	Oldfield Road	98
Trout Creek #3 (Bell)	1902	Adair Road	78
Trout Creek #4 (Urney)	1905	Urney Road from Rockville	64
Trout Creek #5 (Moores Hill)	1923	DeForest Road to West Waterford	60
Ward Creek #2 (McFarlane)	1909	Ward Creek Road	60
Windgap Brook #1	—	Smith Creek Road at Newton	60

MADAWASKA COUNTY

Baker Brook #2 (Morneault)	1939	At Morneault Settlement	95
Baker Brook #3	—	Little River Road 1.3 miles west of Big Reed Road	78
Green River #3 (Boniface)	1925	Davis Road to Green River Road	2 @ 99
Iroquois River #4	1924	3 miles east of Edmundston via Power Road	75
Quisibis River #2	1952	Quisibis Road	57

NORTHUMBERLAND

Barnaby River #2 (O'Donnel)	—	Road: Lower Barnaby River to Semiwagan Ridge	108
Napan River #2 (White)	1923	Whites Lane Cross Road	110
Nelson Hollow (used privately — okay for pictures)	—	At Nelson Hollow (abandoned)	78